MW00487997

Chun Teng Comes to America

by Karen Williams
illustrated by Joanne Renaud

Harcourt
SCHOOL PUBLISHERS

Printed in China

ISBN 10: 0-15-350511-7
ISBN 13: 978-0-15-350511-9

Ordering Options
ISBN 10: 0-15-350334-3 (Grade 4 Below-Level Collection)
ISBN 13: 978-0-15-350334-4 (Grade 4 Below-Level Collection)
ISBN 10: 0-15-357500-X (package of 5)
ISBN 13: 978-0-15-357500-6 (package of 5)

2 3 4 5 6 7 8 9 10   985   12 11 10 09 08 07

My mother and father smiled as the three of us walked out of the immigration station on Angel Island. We had been there for a week, waiting for our interrogation. Then our turn to be questioned finally came, and it had gone well. We knew we had done nothing wrong, but we had still been worried that we would be accused of something. Now we were free to go and live in the United States.

"From here we will take a boat, Chun Teng," my father said to me.

3

My father knew how to do things here in America. He first came to the United States in 1908. Later he returned to China and married my mother, and then they had me. After that, he returned to the United States alone, worked hard, saved his money, and used it to open his own grocery store.

It was now 1922. My father had closed the grocery store so he could return to China to get us. He was finally able to bring us to America.

We rode on the ferryboat to San Francisco. My father had told me that many Chinese people lived there, and that we would, too.

I looked out the window the whole time because I wanted to see what my new country was like. I saw the hills of San Francisco, and I thought they were beautiful. The boat stopped at a pier, and we got off.

"Now we walk to Kearney Street, where Chinatown begins," my father said. "That's the part of San Francisco where many Chinese people live."

On Kearny Street, I looked into the windows of the many little shops. A Chinese girl a little older than me walked past with her father. I averted my eyes from hers because I felt shy.

"There is a Chinese theater," my father said. My mother craned her neck to see over all the people, and then she smiled. It was also her first time in America, and she was looking around at her new home just like I was.

"We turn here to go to the store," my
father said.

We walked down the narrow streets, moving
out of the way of dogs, cats, people on bicycles,
and men pushing carts. At last, we stopped
in front of a small shop. I looked through the
window and saw bags of rice, some herbs, and
other items for sale. "This is my store," my father
said with a smile.

"Where do we live?" I asked.

"Down the street, in an apartment," my father said. It took us just a minute to walk to a small building. My father led us inside to a small apartment that had two little rooms, one sink, and an old stove for cooking. I cringed—how could we ever live in such a small place? Our home in China had had much more space.

My mother looked around and smiled. "This is our new home," she said. Then I felt less worried about living there.

The next day, we walked to the grocery store. At the store, my father showed us what kinds of goods he sold, where he kept them, and how much they cost. He explained that my mother and I would help him run the store so that we could earn more money to get a better place to live. For the next few days, we helped him get the store running again.

One day, about two weeks after we had arrived in Chinatown, my father asked my mother and me to go to a market to buy some fresh fish to sell in the store. Before we left he said to us in a stern voice, "Be very careful. You are going to Stockton Street, which is the edge of Chinatown. You may run into people who do not like Chinese people."

"We'll be all right," my mother said, and we gathered up the money and started on the long walk.

"Look at the fire!" my mother said after we had walked for a while. When we turned the corner we saw a building on fire. Many Chinese men were furiously throwing buckets of water on it to try to put the fire out.

An older Chinese woman came up next to us as we watched. "The fire department doesn't even come here to help us," she said solemnly.

My mother had a pained look on her face as we moved on to the market. Fruits, vegetables, and other foods that came from Asia on boats were brought here. My mother took her time to find the fish my father wanted. She purchased the fish, and then we started our walk back to the store along Stockton Street.

Before we knew it, we saw a group of three American boys walking toward us. My mother grabbed my hand and pulled me close as they approached.

As the boys walked up to us, one of them stopped and stood right in front of me, staring. My mother and I were frightened, so we took a step back. Then the boy took another step and stood in front of me again. My mother and I stepped aside and waited. The boys all burst out laughing and walked on. My mother and I looked at each other, and we quickly turned the corner back into Chinatown.

When we reached the store, we told my father about the boy. "I just don't understand why they act that way!" he cried in a fury.

"I guess it's because they think we are different from them," my mother said.

"Yes, you are probably right," my father said.

I walked to the front window of the store and looked out at the busy street. I could see that America was very different from back home. I knew, though, that I would learn how to live here, and everything would turn out just fine.

Think Critically

1. What are three things that Chun Teng and his parents did in order after leaving Angel Island?

2. Why did Chun Teng's father get upset when Chun Teng and his mother came back from the market?

3. How will Chun Teng's life in America be different than his life in China? How will it be the same?

4. Is this story told in first-person or third-person point of view? How do you know?

5. How did you feel after you read this story?

 Social Studies

Find Out More Chinatown is a neighborhood in San Francisco. Locate San Francisco on a map of California, and find Chinatown, if possible. Use a reference book to learn more about Chinatown. Then write three facts about the neighborhood.

School-Home Connection Discuss this story with a family member. Then have a discussion about why it might be difficult for people to move to a new country.

Word Count: 1,005